S CLUB 7 '7'

Exclusive Distributors

International Music Publications Limited
Griffin House, 161 Hammersmith Road, London W6 8BS, England

International Music Publications GmbH, Germany
Marstallstraße 8, D-80539 Munchen, Germany

Nuova Carisch S.p.A.
Italy: Nuova Carisch Srl, Via Campania 12
20098 San Giuliano Milanese, Milano

France: Carisch Musicom
25 Rue d'Hauteville, 75010 Paris

Spain: Nueva Carisch España
Magallanes 25, 28015 Madrid

www.carisch.com

Danmusik
Vognmagergade 7, DK-1120 Kobenhavn, Denmark

Warner/Chappell Music Australia Pty Ltd.
3 Talavera Road, North Ryde, New South Wales 2113, Australia

Printed by The Panda Group · Haverhill · Suffolk CB9 8PR · UK

Photo Pages: Carter Smith

S
CLUB
7
'7'

Reach

Words and Music by
Cathy Dennis and Andrew Todd

Am
Am(maj7)
(M) When it seems all your hopes and dreams are a mil - lion
Fly a - way, swim the o - cean blue. Drive that
Am7
D
C/D
D
miles a - way I will re - as - sure you.
op - en road, leave the past be - hind you.
C/G
G
We got - ta all stick to - ge - ther. Good friends, there for each - oth - er.
Don't stop, - got - ta keep mov - in'. Your hopes, got - ta keep build - ing.
C/G
D
C/D
D
Nev - er ev - er for - get that I got you and you got

C/D
D
G
D
Em
C
me so (F) reach for the stars.
Climb ev - 'ry moun-
G
D
Em
C
- tain high - er. Reach for the stars.
Fol - low your heart's
G
D
Em
F
de - sire. Reach for the stars.
And when that rain -
C
G/D
- bow's shin - ing ov - er you,
that's when your dreams

1.
D
G
N.C.
will all come true.
2.
G
N.C.
G11
(M) Don't be - lieve in all that you
G
G11
been told.
The sky's the li - mit, you can reach
G
C
Csus2
your goal.
No - one knows just what the fu -
3

Am add9
Am
G
-ture holds.
There ain't no - thing you can't be.
There's a whole
E
A
world at your feet.
I said reach.
(F) Climb ev-'ry moun-tain.
(Reach)
Reach for the moon.
(Reach)
Fol - low that rain - bow
E7
A/E
Bm/E
C♯m/E
D/E
E
D/E
E7
and your dreams will all come true.

A
E
F♯m
D
Reach for the stars.
Climb ev - 'ry moun - tain high - er.
Fol - low your heart's de - sire.
Gmaj7
And when that rain - bow's shin - ing ov -
- er you,
A/E
that's when your dreams will all come true.
Repeat ad lib. to fade

Natural

Words and Music by
Norma Ray, Jean Fredenucci, Cathy Dennis,
and Andrew Todd

F
Fmaj7
Dm
Gm7
D. N. A.
come what may.
It's not by chance we make this per-fect so - lu - tion,
It's in the sci - ence, it's ge - ne - ti - cally pro - ven,
8
C13
C7
A
A7
don't fight it ba - by, you know that it's just des - ti - ny's way.
'cause when you touch me, the re - ac - tion, it just blows me a - way.
Dm
B♭
Csus4
Am7
B♭
Gm7
Ba - by, lov - ing you comes ea - si - ly to me, it's what I'm liv - ing
A7sus4
A7
F6
Dm7
Gm7
Cm7
for, it's all in the che-mis-try. Ba - by, lov - ing you is how it's meant to

1.
F7
B♭maj7
A7sus4
A7
Dm
be, it's some-thing that is oh so na-tu-ral to me, na-tu-ral.
2.
Dm
B♭
Csus4
Am7
B♭
Gm7
me. Ba-by, lov-ing you comes ea-si-ly to me, it's what I'm liv-ing
A7sus4
A7
F6
Dm7
Gm7
Cm7
for, it's all in the che-mis-try. Ba-by, lov-ing you is how it's meant to
F7
B♭maj7
A7sus4
A7
Dm7
be, it's some-thing that is oh so na-tu-ral to me, na-tu-ral.

Dm
Gm
C
F
Fmaj7
Turn off the light, lay your head next to mine,
take it slow-ly, a step at a time.
Dm
Gm7
C11
A
Dm
B♭
Come on get close, get clos-er to me,
it's all so na-tu-ral, it's all so ea-sy to see.
Ba-by, lov-ing
Csus4
Am7
B♭
Gm7
A7sus4
A7
F6
Dm7
you comes ea-si-ly to me, it's what I'm liv-ing for, it's all in the che-mis-try.
Ba-by, lov-ing
Repeat ad lib. to fade
Gm7
Cm7
F7
B♭maj7
A7sus4
A7
Dm
B♭
you is how it's meant to be, it's some-thing that is oh so na-tu-ral to me.
Ba-by lov-ing

I'll Keep Waiting

Words and Music by
Cathy Dennis and Simon Ellis

C
be. Hey girl just a mat - ter of time be - fore you
All this love's too much to un - der - stand
Am
come on home and I get what's mine, 'cause you know
must be a part of a mas - ter plan, but I wish
F
G7
C
G
that you're still my la - dy and your love is gon - na drive me cra - zy.
that it was just that ea - sy 'cause I miss the way you touch and tease me.
C
To think you're gone just makes me wan - na choke,
Damn it girl, why can't you see

Am
you can't fix what you know ain't broke, but I guess
it's not ov - er for you and me.
F
G7
C
G
that I'll just keep wait - ing ev - en though in-side my heart is break - ing.
One day you'll see that you were wrong then you will re - al - ise it was true love all a-long.
Dm7
Am7
G
What you wait - in' for, what you wait - ing for girl?
Dry these tears of rain, dry these tears of rain,
Dm7
Am7
G
C/G
G
Show me love like you did be - fore.
say you'll show me love a - gain.

C
E7
Am
C7
F
G7
C
G
I'll keep wait - ing 'til that day when you come back on home to me.
C
E7
Am
C7
F
G7
C
G
Life's too short to live with - out you, where you are is where I wan - na
G
be. What can I say to change your mind? Think-in' a-bout you all of the time.
Don't keep me hold - ing on, come back to where you be - long.

C
E7(♭9)
Am
C7
F
G7
C
G
I'll keep wait - ing 'til that day when you come back on home to me.
C
E7
Am
C7
F
G7
C
G
Life's too short to live with - out you, where you are is where I wan - na
C
E7(♭9)
Am
C7
F
G7
C
G
I'll keep wait - ing 'til that day when you come back on home to me.
(be.)
Repeat ad lib. to fade
C
B
Am
C7
F
G7
C
G
Life's too short to live with - out you, where you are is where I wan - na

Bring The House Down

Words and Music by
Andy Watkins, Paul Wilson and Tracy Ackerman

E
D/E
A
E
D/E
(1.) draws in let the game be - gin, it's a groove thing.
(2.) in bed with a sleep - y head do - ing no - thing,
E
D/E
A
Let your feet de - cide, gon - na catch a ride, keep on mov -
you can al - ways try just to walk on but it will pull
E
D/E
C♯m7
F♯m9
- 'in. So let's go a - way, the mood
you in. We're fly - ing a - way, we fall
C♯m7
F♯m9
Gmaj7
can't be that hard to reach, the night will just take us there.
in - to this fan - ta - sy where the groove will car - ry us on.

Em
F♯m
G
A
Em
F♯m
G
A
And all you got - ta do is, all you got - ta do is bring the
E
Bm7/E
A
E
D/E
house down, raise the roof and get on the floor.
E
Bm7/E
A
Let's bring the house down, real - ly want to hear you shout-ing
E
D/E
1.
E
2.
E
D/E
more, more, more.
2. You stay
Ev -

D
E
-'ry - bo - dy do your thing, lets bring the house down.
D/E
Ev - 'ry bo - dy spread your wings, let's bring the
D
E
house down.
So let's go a - way,
C♯m7
F♯m9
the mood
can't be that hard to reach,
C♯m7
F♯m9
the night will just take us there
Gmaj7

Em
F♯m
G
A
Em
F♯m
G
A
and all you got to do is, all you got to do is bring the
E
Bm7/E
A
E
D/E
house down, raise the roof and get on the floor.
E
Bm7/E
A
Let's bring the house down, real - ly want to hear you shout-ing
E
D/E
Repeat ad lib. to fade
more, more, more. Let's bring the

Best Friend

Words and Music by
Timothy Laws, Stephen Emmanuel
and Bradley McIntosh

E♭
Fm
B♭m7
Cm7
say we were the trou-ble-some two,
and all the girls liked me and you.
chill-in' with the la - dies,
those times were the great-est.
I can nev-er for-get the times you co-vered my back,
helped me out, you cut me some slack, there was
So don't wor-ry 'bout a thing my friend,
'cause you can count on me, thick or thin,
noth-ing you would nev - er do,
it's all a-bout me and you.
'cause I'll be there right to the end,
'til the end.
You're my
Fm7
Fm/C
bro - ther, you're my sis - ter, we'll stick to - geth - er, no mat-ter what, no mat-ter what. Best

Fm7 Fm Fm/C B♭m7 Cm7
friend, never gonna let you down. Best friend, always gonna be around. You
Fm7 Fm Fm/C B♭m7 Cm7
know whatever life puts you through, I'll be there for you. We all need a
Fm7 Fm Fm/C B♭m7 Cm7
best friend to understand. A best friend to take your hand. 'Cause you
Fm7 Fm Fm/C B♭m7 Cm7
know whatever life puts you through, I'll be there for you.

E♭ Fm B♭m7 Cm7 E♭ Fm B♭m7 Cm7
Come on, come on, best friends. Come on, come on, best friends.
E♭ Fm B♭m7 Cm7 E♭ Fm B♭m7 Cm7
Come on, come on, best friends. Come on, come on, best friends. You're my
Fm7 Fm Fm/C B♭m7 Cm7
bro - ther, you're my sis - ter, we'll stick to -
1. 2.
Fm7 Fm Fm/C B♭m7 Cm7 B♭m7 Cm7
- geth - er, no mat - ter what, no mat-ter what. You're my no mat-ter what. Best

Fm7 Fm Fm/C B♭m7 Cm7
friend, never gon-na let you down. Best friend, al-ways gon-na be a-round. You
Fm7 Fm Fm/C B♭m7 Cm7
know what-ev-er life puts you through, I'll be there for you. We all need a
Fm7 Fm Fm/C B♭m7 Cm7
best friend to un-der-stand, a best friend to take your hand. 'Cause you
Fm7 Fm Fm/C B♭m7 Cm7
Repeat ad lib. to fade
know what-ev-er life puts you through, I'll be there for you. Best

All In Love Is Fair

Words and Music by
Cathy Dennis and Simon Ellis

Fm7
C
1. First he said that he would - n't leave me, what a fool to be-lieve that line,
2. First you said that you would - n't cheat me, that our love was to last all time,
Fm7add11
C
just an-oth - er one of his ob - ses - sions to help to pass the time.
she must have been a big ex - cep - tion if you're not the cheat - ing kind.
Fm7
A♭m
Get it right, get it right, get it right – don't get it wrong, 'cause if you
Get it right, get it right, get it right – don't get it wrong, 'cause if you
Fm9
Fm6
Fm9
Fm6
A♭dim
Cmaj9
C
want me get your ass on ov - er here and show me.
want me get your ass on ov - er here and show me.

Cadd9
C
Fm9
Fm6
Fm9
Fm6
A♭dim
Stop wast - ing time, — and if you need me, — get your act to - geth - er boy and
Stop wast - ing time, — boy if you knew me, — ba - by, you would nev - er want to
Cmaj9
C
Cadd9
C
Fm6
Fm
show me, — you should be mine.
lose me — – make up your mind.
All in love is fair, one of us will
Cadd9
C
Fm9
Fm6
Fm
C
lose. Is it her or me, is it me or you? Who's it gon - na
Fm6
Fm
Cadd9
C
Fm9
Fm6
Fm
C
be, what you gon - na do, are you ov - er me? I'm not ov - er you.

C
Fm6
Fm
Spoken rap: Ah, you got-ta take the good with the bad, the hap-py with the sad, but
Cadd9
C
Fm9
Fm6
Fm
don't get mad if things don't go the way you planned it, just un-der-stand that real love is in de-mand. If you're
C
Fm6
Fm
rea-dy for com-mit-ment girl just take my hand. If you get luck-y, love will be a cruise. There are
Cadd9
C
Fm9
Fm6
Fm
so ma-ny roads, which one you gon-na choose? But there's a risk you know you got-ta take,

C
Fm9
Fm6
Fm
no mess-ing, a choice you got-ta make. The one cross you know you got-ta bear –
C
Fm6
Fm
Cadd9
C
all in love is fair. All in love is fair, one of us will lose. Is it her or
Fm9
Fm6
Fm
C
Fm6
Fm
me, is it me or you? Who's it gon-na be, what you gon-na
Cadd9
C
Fm9
Fm6
Fm
C
Repeat ad lib. to fade
do, are you ov-er me? I'm not ov-er you. All in love is

Love Train

Words and Music by
Cathy Dennis and Andrew Todd

B♭
Fm7
B♭
Fm7
I think it's time I should be mov - ing on.
did I reach my ba - by in the tun - nel of love.
I'm gon - na do the
I'm gon - na do the
Cm7
F
Cm7
F
right thing, I'm gon - na do the right thing, you know that it's the
right thing, I know that it's the right thing, ooh, you make my
Dm7
Gm
A♭
E♭/G
A♭
E♭/G
A♭
best thing.
heart sing.
I've got my - self a one - way tick - et and I'm
F
B♭/F
F
F11
B♭
Fm7
com - ing home, rid - ing the love train, mak - ing my way back to you ba -

B♭
Fm7
F11
B♭
Fm7
- by.
Rid - ing the love train, cruis - ing my way back
Gm
F
F11
B♭
Fm7
to my ba - by's arms.
Rid - ing the love train, mak - ing my way back to you ba -
B♭
Fm7
F11
B♭
Fm7
- by.
Rid - ing the love train, cruis - ing my way back
Gm
F
A♭
E♭/G
A♭
E♭/G
A♭add9
where my ba - by's arms are wait - ing for me.

B♭
Fm7
B♭
Fm7
Ooh, ooh, ooh.
C
Gm7
C
Gm7
1.
Love train, wait - ing for the love train, love train, wait - ing for the love train.
2.
Gm7
C
Gm7
C
Gm7
- ing for the love train. Love train, mak - ing my way back to you ba - by.
G11
C
Gm7
Am
G
Rid - ing the love train, cruis - ing my way back to my ba - by's arms.

G11
C
Gm7
Rid - ing the love train, mak - ing my way back to you ba -
C
Gm7
G11
C
Gm7
- by.
Rid - ing the love train, cruis -
1.
Am
G
F11
- ing my way back to my ba - by's arms.
Rid - ing the
2.
Am
G
G11
C
to my ba - by's arms, back to you ba - by.
Love train.

Cross My Heart

Words and Music by
Andy Watkins, Paul Wilson
and Tracy Ackerman

Fm
B♭m7
E♭
C
Fm
B♭m9
'Cos I need you more and more, 'cause you're my life and I live for your
You're there so deep in - side and I like what I feel, though it's
E♭
Cm
Fm
B♭m7
E♭
C7sus4
love that you give, and al - though my jour - ney's long, I'll soon be home.
not al - ways real it helps me car - ry on 'til I come home.
B♭m11
E♭
Oh, it's gon - na be so hard on my
B♭m11
E♭
C
oh,
own, but I won't be a - lone.

Fm
B♭m7
E♭
Cm7
Cross my heart and tell no lies, no - one's leav - ing you be - hind,
Fm
B♭m7
E♭
C7sus4
Fm
B♭m7
just be - cause we said good - bye. Ba - by, cross my heart, I do be - lieve,
E♭
Cm7
Fm
B♭m7
E♭
C7sus4
in my thoughts and in my dreams, I'll be tak - ing you with me, ba - by.
D♭maj7
Cm7
B♭m7
Dream a dream, a dream, a dream, a dream - ing where - ev - er you are you're near me.

D♭maj7
Cm7
C7
Please be - lieve, be - lieve, be - lieve, be - lieve in whatever I say. I cross my
Fm
B♭m7
E♭
Cm7
heart,
ba - by,
Cross my heart and tell no lies, no - one's leav - ing you be - hind,
Fm
B♭m7
E♭
C7sus4
Fm
B♭m7
woah, ba - by.
I do be - lieve
just be - cause we said good - bye, ba - by.
Cross my heart, I do be - lieve,
Repeat ad lib. to fade
E♭
Cm7
Fm
B♭m7
E♭
C7sus4
in my thoughts and in my dreams, I'll be tak - ing you with me. Ba - by

The Colour Of Blue

Words and Music by
Lars Aass and Bottolf Lødemel

F7sus4
F7
B♭m7
E♭
who's gon - na be my lov - er for life, my ba - by, be there to hold
So nev - er go for less than a per - fect thing, seek and then hope -
B♭m7
E♭7sus4
E♭7
A♭
me through the night. When it hap - pens you can see
- ful - ly you'll find there's a rhy - thm and a rhyme,
G7
G♭6
F7sus4
F7
it in his eyes, they tell no lies, bright - er than the
you've got to find it, then you'll see. 'Cause ba - by we could
B♭m7
E♭
B♭m7
sky in Ju - ly, my ba - by, cool - er than a - ny - one I've known.
go on all night, just danc - ing, do - ing it 'til the break of dawn.

E♭7sus4
E♭7
A♭
B♭7
The col-our of blue, re-minds me of you, I nev-er see grey,
D♭m
A♭
E♭/G
Fm7
green, black you're true. The col-our of blue, no oth-er will do,
B♭7
D♭m
1.
D♭m/E
G♭add9
in my heart, on-ly feel the col-our of blue.
A♭
2.
D♭m/E
G♭add9
2. I say if on-ly feel the col-our of blue.

Fm7
B♭7
D♭m
D♭m/E♭
A♭
In the rain - bow I can see colours of mis - be - lief.
There is on - ly one for me
D♭m6
Emaj7
G♭
and it will for - ev - er be.
E♭/G
Ooh, ooh, hey,

B♭7
D♭m
D♭m/E
G♭7
hey.
The col - our of blue,
A♭
B♭7
D♭m
re - minds me of you,
I nev - er see grey, green, black, you're true.
A♭
E♭/G
Fm7
B♭7
The col - our of blue,
no - oth - er will do,
in my heart.
D♭m
1.
D♭m/E
G♭add9
2.
D♭m/E
G♭add9
A♭
The col - our of blue.

I'll Be There

Words and Music by
Cathy Dennis and Danny D

Gm/B♭
F
C
G
Gm/B♭
F
do, do, do, do, do, do, do, do,
do, do, do, do, do, do, do,
do, do, do, do, do, do, do, do.
Am
Em7
Gm
Dm7
1. Look-ing in my me-mo-ry what did I see? All the good times you gave to me.
2. What I think, I'd be lost with-out you, makes me won-der what I did be-fore you.
Eve-nings in the park, way af - ter dark, lis - ten to the ra - di - o in my car. It's
When it mat-tered you were there for me, you were my rock boy, you were my en - er - gy.
times like these you see the wood from the trees, you come to my aid when I'm on my knees.
Time flies, but I'll nev - er for-get the way it was the day we met.

Am
Em7
Gm
Dm7
Next time you feel a-lone, just pick up the phone. Reach out and touch,
Don't be sur-prised, you know it's true, I'm gon-na be there for you.
C
G
B♭maj7
F
whis-per my name, I will de-liv-er a-gain and a-gain.
Straight from the heart, ho-nest and true, I'll pro-mise you this
I will be there for you. I'll be there for you.
1.
2.
Through the sun,

Am
Em7
Gm6
Dm9
Am
Em7
through the rain, I will still feel the same. Be it good, be it bad, I'll al - ways
Gm6
Gm9
Am
Em7
Gm6
Gm9
un - der - stand. When you're down, when you're blue, I will be there for you. 'Cause
Am
Em7
Gm6
Gm9
no - bo - dy does it bet - ter, we're gon - na get there to - geth - er.
Am
Em7
Gm
Dm7
Am
Em7
Through the sun and through the rain, I'll be there for you. Through the sun and through the rain, I'll

Gm
Dm7
Am
Em7
Gm
Dm7
be there, I'll be there for you. No - bo - dy, no - bo-dy does it bet - ter to - geth - er,
Am
Em7
Gm
Dm7
C
G
no - bo - dy, no - bo-dy does it bet - ter. Reach out and touch, whis-per my name,
B♭maj7
F
C
G
B♭maj7
F
I will de - liv - er a - gain and a - gain. Straight from the heart,
C
G
B♭maj7
F
C
G
B♭maj7
F
Repeat ad lib. to fade
ho-nest and true, I'll pro-mise you this, I will be there for you, Reach out and touch,

Stand By You

Words and Music by
Remee and Kristian Holger

F C B♭ F/A C7 F C B♭ F/A C7
stand by you, if you want me to. I'm gon-na stand by you, if you want it to - night.
F C B♭ F/A C7 F C B♭ F/A C
I will stand by you, 'cause I want to be with you. I'll stand by you, stand by you.
F C B♭ F/A C7 F C B♭ F/A C7
Stand by, stand by you (stand by you). Stand by, stand by you (stand by you).
F C B♭ F/A C7 F C
Stand by, stand by you (stand by you). Stand by,

B♭
F/A
C7
F
N.C.
B♭
N.C.
stand by you. I on-ly want to be with you, I on-ly want to be with you.
F
C
Gm
Dm7
F
C
Damn you, don't you know it's so good to-geth-er, us two.
Gm
Dm7
F
C
Gm
Dm7
No-thing's gon-na come in be-tween us. I know we go in two dif-ferent di-rec-
F
C
Gm
Dm7
Am
-tions some-times, but you will al-ways be on my mind. And if you think

Dm
Am
B♭
you 'aint got no - bo - dy,
I just want you to know,
F
C
B♭
F/A
C7
F
C
B♭
F/A
C7
if you want me to,
I'm gon-na stand by you,
if you want it to - night.
F
C
B♭
F/A
C7
F
C
B♭
F/A
C7
I will stand by you,
'cause I want to be with you.
I'll stand by you,
stand by you.
F
C
B♭
F/A
C7
F
C
Stand by,
stand by you (stand by you).
Stand by,

B♭ F/A C7 F C B♭ F/A C7
stand by you (stand by). Stand by, stand by you (stand by you
F C B♭ F/A C7 F
N.C.
). Stand by, stand by you. Woah, I'm gon - na
G♭ D♭ C♭ G♭/B♭ D♭7 G♭ D♭
stand - by you, if you want me to. I'm gon - na stand by you,
C♭ G♭/B♭ D♭7 G♭ D♭ C♭ G♭/B♭ D♭7
if you want it to - night. I will stand by you, 'cause I want to be with

G♭ D♭ C♭ G♭/B♭ D♭7 G♭ D♭ C♭ G♭/B♭ D♭7
— you. I'll stand by — you, stand by — you. Stand by, — stand by you (stand by — you —
G♭ D♭ C♭ G♭/B♭ D♭7 G♭ D♭
—). Stand by, — stand by you (stand by — you). Stand by, —
C♭ G♭/B♭ D♭7 G♭ D♭ C♭ G♭/B♭ D♭7
stand by you. (Oh — yeah.) Stand by, — stand by you. 'Cause I
C♭ G♭/B♭ A♭m7 G♭ N.C. C♭ G♭
want to be with — you, I'll stand by — you. 'Cause I want to be with — you, I'll stand by — you.

Spiritual Love

Words and Music by
Peter Akinrinlola and Rodney Green

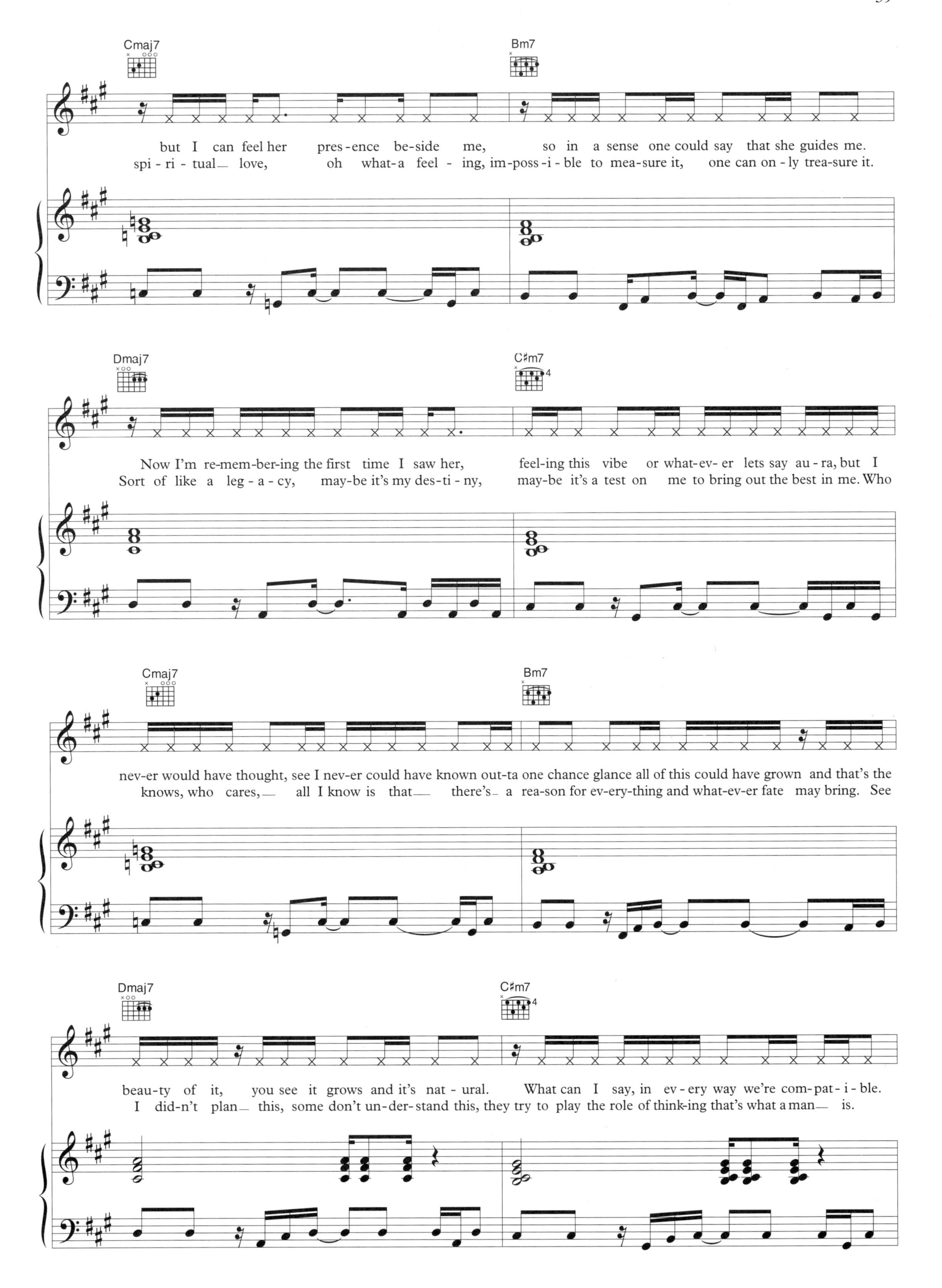
Cmaj7
Bm7
but I can feel her pres-ence be-side me, so in a sense one could say that she guides me.
spi-ri-tual love, oh what-a feel-ing, im-poss-i-ble to mea-sure it, one can on-ly trea-sure it.
Dmaj7
C♯m7
Now I'm re-mem-ber-ing the first time I saw her, feel-ing this vibe or what-ev-er lets say au-ra, but I
Sort of like a leg-a-cy, may-be it's my des-ti-ny, may-be it's a test on me to bring out the best in me. Who
Cmaj7
Bm7
nev-er would have thought, see I nev-er could have known out-ta one chance glance all of this could have grown and that's the
knows, who cares, all I know is that there's a rea-son for ev-ery-thing and what-ev-er fate may bring. See
Dmaj7
C♯m7
beau-ty of it, you see it grows and it's nat-ural. What can I say, in ev-ery way we're com-pat-i-ble.
I did-n't plan this, some don't un-der-stand this, they try to play the role of think-ing that's what a man is.

Cmaj7
Bm7
Talk is cheap, at times we don't speak – that's right, 'cos we're en-grossed in thoughts that are deep,– it's like
To me she's more than just a fash-ion ac-ces-sor-y and I'll pro-tect her by a-ny-means nec-es-sa-ry–
Dmaj7
C♯m7
two hearts, two minds, two bo-dies, two souls mak-ing one whole. Now it's got-ta be told
Cmaj7
Bm7
that what we have is more than just phy-si-cal, don't be so cy-ni-cal. We got a-spi-ri-tual
Dmaj7
C♯m7
Cmaj7
love. Feels so na-tu-tral, more than phy-si-cal, spi-ri-tual love.

Bm7
Dmaj7
C♯m7
Feels so na - tu - ral,
more than phy - si - cal,
1.
Cmaj7
Bm7
spi - ri - tual love.
2. You got - ta, you got - ta
2.
Cmaj7
Bm7
spi - ri - tual love,
love,
Dmaj7
C♯m7
Cmaj7
love.
Hey,
can you feel it?
It's so

Bm7
Dmaj7
C♯m7
na - tu - ral.
Ho, you know you mean it, you know you mean it, ba - by.
Cmaj7
Bm7
Dmaj7
Spi - ri - tual love, we've got a spi - ri - tual love, feels so na - tu - ral,
C♯m7
Cmaj7
Bm7
more than phy - si - cal.
Spi - ri - tual love,
Dmaj7
C♯m7
feels so na - tu - ral, more than phy - si - cal.

Printed in England
The Panda Group · Haverhill · Suffolk · 10/00